My Beautiful Life

Daily Journal for Inspirational Living

By Trez Ibrahim

Silver Laurel Publishing House
California

SILVER LAUREL
PUBLISHING HOUSE

www.SilverLaurelPublishing.com

My Beautiful Life
Daily Journal for Inspirational Living

By Trez Ibrahim
Life Mastery Solution
www.TrezIbrahim.com

Published by Silver Laurel Publishing House
360 East First Street, Suite 426
Tustin, CA 92780
www.SilverLaurelPublishing.com

ISBN: 978-0-9974377-5-1

Printed in the United States of America 10 9 8 7 6 5 4 3 2

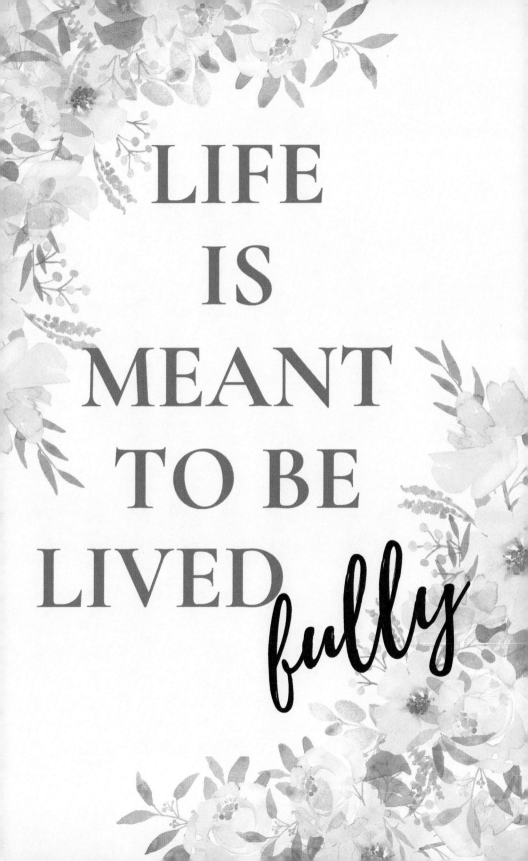

Welcome to your Beautiful Journey.

I want to warmly welcome you here. I am so thrilled that you are allowing me the privilege of joining you on your journey towards greatness; stepping into the life you know you are meant to be living and for saying YES to success, YES to mastery and YES to your dreams.

My life's work is about teaching men and women just like you to Think and Aim Big and Achieve Success Beyond Your Wildest Dreams.

When you think of success, do you envision oodles of money, a mansion, and a fancy sports car? Those items are great, and even more meaningful when you have a deeper sense of achievement and fulfillment . . . beyond your wildest dreams.

I believe true Life Mastery is when you are living at a 10 in every area of your life. This means you are in a career that brings you great joy, you are making the money you desire to live the lifestyle you love and have the free time to enjoy it. You have extraordinary relationships, are feeling healthy and vibrant so that you can revel in your success, and are able to be, do and have the things that connect you to your greater purpose.

Living an Inspired Life is different for every person – for some, it's lots of money, and for others, it's fulfillment and for others it's freedom. Some people want to live in a mansion overlooking the ocean, while others want to live in a cottage by the lake or down at the farm.

Success is what you say it is.

Want to know something even more powerful? Success is even what you say it isn't. Yes, you can and often do get in your own way. This journey is about defining what you want and placing your attention and intention on it and it alone.

As you define success, I invite you to ask yourself the one question guaranteed to put you on the right path, the path of your higher purpose.

The question . . . What would I love?

Trez Ibrahim

TREZ IBRAHIM
LifeMasterySolution.com

"A journey of a thousand miles begins with a single step"
~Chinese Proverb

I invite you to commit to this journey. As the saying goes, every dream begins with a small step, a small commitment, a small YES to yourself. Then you take the next step, then the next, and before you know it, you will be so much closer to your dream than you could have ever imagined.

In this journey, you need not know all the steps, you need only be willing to say YES and commit to the dream. In this journal, you will be guided to commit to living An Inspired Life, one that gives you purpose, joy and full-fillment. One that provides direction and a reminder of the Beautiful Life awaiting you. One that keeps you centered and focused so that your subconscious mind, spirit or your higher self, will draw to you the resources and opportunities available to turn possibilities into probabilities.

This is not a one shot deal. This is not a get rich quick or immediate gratification system. This is a tool that I invite you to use every single day to become the creator of your life. This is a powerful life skill of getting focused on what you desire, opening up to your higher mind that is calling you to be greater. This is the evolutionary instinct within you to show up as your Greatest Self.

Congratulations for taking this first step. I encourage you to continue to walk towards your Dream and please share your journey with me. I want to hear it all, the wins, the trials, the challenges and the triumphs. Share your story with me at Trez@LifeMasterySolution.com .

YOUR GUIDE FOR GETTING THE MOST BENEFIT FROM THIS

Journal

"Start your day with good intentions and set yourself up for a good attitude. It's not what happens to you that matters but how you respond."
~Kenneth H. Blanchard

MORNING INTENTIONS . . .

Morning Intentions give you an opportunity to set the energy or tone of the day. It provides time to get clear on what is important to you and what is required in order for you to be full-filled. Full-fillment is about feeling full in all areas of your life, taking care of all your human needs and nurturing the mental, physical, emotional, and spiritual sides of you.

"Self-doubt is when you think you are not good enough. Self-confidence is when you are crazy enough to believe that you are the best."
~Michael Bassey Johnson

I Am . . .

What you put behind the words "I AM" becomes your destiny. Whatever follows "I AM" follows you. When you say I Am smart, confident, beautiful, then you open up to a world where you find evidence of being smart, confident, and beautiful. Those two powerful words determine your identity. Your identity determines your thoughts, your thoughts dictate your choices, your choices determine your behaviors and actions and your behaviors and actions determine your results, your life. In the morning, I invite you to ask yourself, who are you required to be in order to show up as the best highest version of yourself today. Write that word or words behind the words "I AM".

Example:

I AM Confident
I AM Powerful
I AM Kind

I ENJOY . . .

Life is about enjoyment, full-fillment, fun. There is a little girl and little boy in each of us and that inner child needs to find love and joy in every moment in life. Remember the time when you were mesmerized by the bee hovering over a flower, or that time when you laughed uncontrollably while playing peek a boo with a loved one. Get in touch with him or her and ask, what would be fun, what would you enjoy, what would get you up and excited to get through your day.

Example:

I Enjoy laughter while watching a funny movie
I Enjoy watching a beautiful sunset
I Enjoy going for a swim in the lake

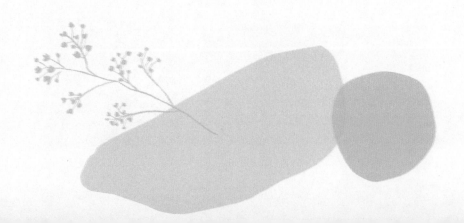

"Discover the joy of giving and you will discover the reason for living."
~Mark Victor Hansen

I gIve . . .

There is an innate part of us that knows we are part of a whole. That part of us needs to feel connected and needs to give. Giving reminds us of the abundance we are surrounded by. The apple tree gives freely, knowing there are more fruits to offer. It doesn't hold back, it continues to proliferate. Giving announces to the Universe that you recognize the unlimited abundance available to you. Today, ask yourself, what can I give? It may be a smile, a helping hand or compliment.

Example:

I Give money to the disaster relief organization
I Give a hug to my elderly neighbor
I Give a home cooked meal to my parents

I COMPLETE . . .

We all need to feel a sense of accomplishment. Especially if you are a business owner or entrepreneur, you never feel complete since there is always more to do. Today, I invite you to ask yourself, what is the one thing that if completed, will give you the sense of completion. It may be something you have been putting off, something you have been procrastinating on, something that is nagging at you. These incompletes tend to drain us of our precious creative energy since our subconscious is constantly thinking about that thing that you should be doing. It may be to call the accountant to get your taxes done, send the proposal to the dream client, or clean out your car's center console. However big or small, write it down and get it done. What you will find is once you complete this, you will be able to breathe more deeply, have more space for yourself and feel a weight of anxiety lifted off you.

Example:

I complete making the appointment to get my oil changed
I complete sending the thank you card for my gift
I complete making the appointment with my boss to ask for a raise

I FORGIVE . . .

Any farmer knows soil must be as healthy as the seed for the crop to prosper. You can't grow a healthy dream in toxic soil. Even the best dream cannot survive if it is planted in soil that is toxic with resentment. Everyone has forgiveness work to do – it's a mental, emotional and spiritual practice that opens the doors for your life and frees us to live a life worth living. Even once you make a conscious decision to forgive someone for whom you harbor some resentment, resentment can creep back in. And while it doesn't change your past, it changes your present and transforms your future. Today, ask yourself, who are you holding onto some form or anger, bitterness or resentment. It may be your co-worker, your spouse or even the person who cut you off on the road. If thinking about them brings up negative emotions, you are giving your precious energy away to them. You need only write their name or reference them. We are not excusing the actions, we are letting go of our hold on the person. Forgiveness allows you to call back your energy so that you can use it to live the life you love.

Example:

I Forgive Bob
I Forgive Susan
I Forgive the bank teller

"Be thankful for what you have, you'll end up having more."
~Oprah Winfrey

I AM GRATEFUL FOR...

I believe we live in a "More" Universe. When we acknowledge something wonderful in our lives, the Universe responds with more of the same. By the same token, when we focus on what is not working or what is missing, the Universe brings us more of the lack or undesired circumstance. Today, choose blessings over difficulties, focus on the good versus the bad and be grateful for all the wonderful things in your life, big and small. What or who are you grateful for? Write at least 5 things you are grateful for and watch your life continue to be blessed with more.

Example:

I Am Grateful for my son
I Am Grateful for the roof over my head
I Am Grateful for the sun shining through my window this morning

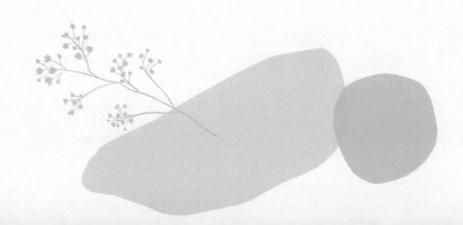

"In the absence of clearly-defined goals, we become strangely loyal to performing daily trivia until ultimately we become enslaved by it"
~Robert A. Heinlein

my 3 MONTH GOALS . . .

What are your 3 month goals? This should be an extension of your big vision and your big harry audacious goals. Writing your 3 month goals here sets your intention and attention on those 3 things that you are set on accomplishing within the next 90 days. As a bonus, make every day move in the direction of your goals.

"If my mind can conceive it, if my heart can believe it, then I can achieve it."
~Muhammad Ali

MY WILD OUTRAGEOUS GOALS . . .

Here, you are invited to stretch. A dream is meant to grow you into the person you are meant to be. If what you were doing were enough to get what you want, what you want would have already shown up. You are an incredible infinite being with a gift to share to the world. You are a powerful person who is meant to step into that knowingness. You are not meant to stay small, you are not meant to dim your light and you are not meant to be complacent with life as it is. I invite you to ask yourself, if not even the sky was the limit, what would you love? If you knew you couldn't fail, what would you want to be, do or have? What brings you joy? Think big, think outrageous, and write it down.

"Either you run your day or the day runs you"
~Jim Rohn

INTENTION FOR THE DAY . . .

Most people have heard of the idea that your thoughts have something to do with your life; that your thoughts create your reality. Yet, most people don't take the time to create their day the way they would love. Setting intentions allows for the flow and ease in life. When you set an intention in the morning, you determine where your focus will be. That focus will allow you to see the people, resources and opportunities to make real that which you desire. In this section, I invite you to write out your day as if it has already happened. What would have to happen for you to say, "This was a fabulous day".

Example:

I am so happy and grateful for my amazing successful and fun day. The meeting with my new client was so inspiring and I'm happy to say she said yes to our offer. I had an incredible lunch with my partner celebrating the win and ended my day with an energizing workout that left me feeling healthy, vibrant and alive.

"We all need encouragement! You are doing a fabulous job! No matter how hard the journey may be, remember to be kind to yourself. You are doing the best you can! You are amazing and beautiful every day! Don't ever tell yourself anything less!"
~Erin Bella Bleue

WINS FOR THE DAY . . .

A high achiever's job is never done. This is why it is imperative that we give ourselves credit for our accomplishments. We need to acknowledge and recognize our wins. We are required to celebrate the fact that we got done what we said we were going to get done. Before moving on to the next project, next to do item or next task, take a few minutes each evening to celebrate your wins, acknowledge those completions and give yourself the high five that you so deserve that will keep you motivated to continue moving toward your dreams and goals.

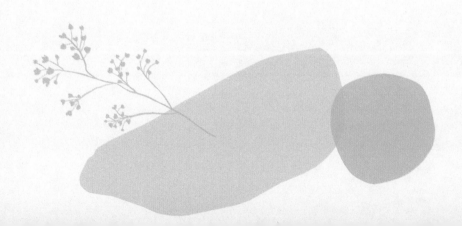

YOUR

JOURNEY

Begins

My Beautiful Morning

"The future belongs to those who believe in the beauty of their dreams."

~Eleanor Roosevelt

Date: _____

Morning Intentions

I am ....

I enjoy ....

I give ....

I complete ....

I forgive ....

I am grateful for . . .

1. ....

2. ....

3. ....

4. ....

5. ....

My 3 month goals . . .

1. ....
2. ....
3. ....

My wild outrageous goals . . .

1. ....
2. ....
3. ....
4. ....
5. ....
6. ....
7. ....
8. ....
9. ....
10. ....

My intention for today . . .

....
....
....
....

Evening Reflection . . . Wins for the day

1. ....
2. ....
3. ....
4. ....
5. ....

My Beautiful Morning

"Happiness is the key to success. If you love what you are doing, you will be successful."

~Albert Schweitzer

Date:

Morning Intentions

I am ....

I enjoy ....

I give ....

I complete ....

I forgive ....

I am grateful for . . .

1. ....

2. ....

3. ....

4. ....

5. ....

My 3 month goals . . .

1. ....
2. ....
3. ....

My wild outrageous goals . . .

1. ....
2. ....
3. ....
4. ....
5. ....
6. ....
7. ....
8. ....
9. ....
10. ....

My intention for today . . .

....
....
....
....

Evening Reflection . . . Wins for the day

1. ....
2. ....
3. ....
4. ....
5. ....

My Beautiful Morning

"Every great dream begins with a dreamer.
Always remember, you have within you, the
strength, the patience and the passion to reach
for the stars to change the world."
~Harriet Tubman

Date:

Morning Intentions

I am ....

I enjoy ....

I give ....

I complete ....

I forgive ....

I am grateful for . . .

1. ....

2. ....

3. ....

4. ....

5. ....

My 3 month goals . . .

1. ....
2. ....
3. ....

My wild outrageous goals . . .

1. ....
2. ....
3. ....
4. ....
5. ....
6. ....
7. ....
8. ....
9. ....
10. ....

My intention for today . . .

....
....
....
....
....

Evening Reflection . . . Wins for the day

1. ....
2. ....
3. ....
4. ....
5. ....

My Beautiful Morning

"Whatever you do, or dream you can, begin it. Boldness has genius and power and magic in it."
~Johann Wolfgang von Goethe

Date:

Morning Intentions

I am ....

I enjoy ....

I give ....

I complete ....

I forgive ....

I am grateful for . . .

1. ....

2. ....

3. ....

4. ....

5. ....

My 3 month goals . . .

1. ....
2. ....
3. ....

My wild outrageous goals . . .

1. ....
2. ....
3. ....
4. ....
5. ....
6. ....
7. ....
8. ....
9. ....
10. ....

My intention for today . . .

....
....
....
....

Evening Reflection . . . Wins for the day

1. ....
2. ....
3. ....
4. ....
5. ....

My Beautiful Morning

"Dare to live the life you have dreamed for yourself. Go forward and make your dreams come true."

~Ralph Waldo

Date:

Morning Intentions

I am ....

I enjoy ....

I give ....

I complete ....

I forgive ....

I am grateful for . . .

1. ....

2. ....

3. ....

4. ....

5. ....

My 3 month goals . . .

1. ....
2. ....
3. ....

My wild outrageous goals . . .

1. ....
2. ....
3. ....
4. ....
5. ....
6. ....
7. ....
8. ....
9. ....
10. ....

My intention for today . . .

....
....
....
....
....

Evening Reflection . . . Wins for the day

1. ....
2. ....
3. ....
4. ....
5. ....

My Beautiful Morning

"Success is steady progress toward one's personal goals."

~Jim Rohn

Date:

Morning Intentions

I am ....

I enjoy ....

I give ....

I complete ....

I forgive ....

I am grateful for . . .

1. ....

2. ....

3. ....

4. ....

5. ....

My 3 month goals . . .

1. ....
2. ....
3. ....

My wild outrageous goals . . .

1. ....
2. ....
3. ....
4. ....
5. ....
6. ....
7. ....
8. ....
9. ....
10. ....

My intention for today . . .

....
....
....
....

Evening Reflection . . . Wins for the day

1. ....
2. ....
3. ....
4. ....
5. ....

My Beautiful Morning

"Set your goals high, and don't stop
till you get there."

~Bo Jackson

Date:

Morning Intentions

I am ....

I enjoy ....

I give ....

I complete ....

I forgive ....

I am grateful for . . .

1. ....

2. ....

3. ....

4. ....

5. ....

My 3 month goals . . .

1. ....
2. ....
3. ....

My wild outrageous goals . . .

1. ....
2. ....
3. ....
4. ....
5. ....
6. ....
7. ....
8. ....
9. ....
10. ....

My intention for today . . .

....
....
....
....

Evening Reflection . . . Wins for the day

1. ....
2. ....
3. ....
4. ....
5. ....

My Beautiful Morning

"The people who are crazy enough to think
they can change the world are
the ones who do."

~Steve Jobs

Date:

Morning Intentions

I am ....

I enjoy ....

I give ....

I complete ....

I forgive ....

I am grateful for . . .

1. ....

2. ....

3. ....

4. ....

5. ....

My 3 month goals . . .

1. ....
2. ....
3. ....

My wild outrageous goals . . .

1. ....
2. ....
3. ....
4. ....
5. ....
6. ....
7. ....
8. ....
9. ....
10. ....

My intention for today . . .

....
....
....
....

Evening Reflection . . . Wins for the day

1. ....
2. ....
3. ....
4. ....
5. ....

My Beautiful Morning

"Success. . . is the result of preparation,
hard work, and learning from failure."

~Colin Powell

Date:

Morning Intentions

I am ....

I enjoy ....

I give ....

I complete ....

I forgive ....

I am grateful for . . .

1. ....

2. ....

3. ....

4. ....

5. ....

My 3 month goals . . .

1. ....
2. ....
3. ....

My wild outrageous goals . . .

1. ....
2. ....
3. ....
4. ....
5. ....
6. ....
7. ....
8. ....
9. ....
10. ....

My intention for today . . .

....
....
....
....
....

Evening Reflection . . . Wins for the day

1. ....
2. ....
3. ....
4. ....
5. ....

My Beautiful Morning

"Hope lies in dreams, in imagination, and in the courage of those who dare to make dreams into reality."

~Jonas Salk

Date:

Morning Intentions

I am ....

I enjoy ....

I give ....

I complete ....

I forgive ....

I am grateful for . . .

1. ....

2. ....

3. ....

4. ....

5. ....

My 3 month goals . . .

1. ....
2. ....
3. ....

My wild outrageous goals . . .

1. ....
2. ....
3. ....
4. ....
5. ....
6. ....
7. ....
8. ....
9. ....
10. ....

My intention for today . . .

....
....
....
....

Evening Reflection . . . Wins for the day

1. ....
2. ....
3. ....
4. ....
5. ....

My Beautiful Morning

Goals are like a map. They help us determine
where we want to end up, and give us
personal direction on which to
focus our energy."
~Catherine Pulsifer

Date:

Morning Intentions

I am ....

I enjoy ....

I give ....

I complete ....

I forgive ....

I am grateful for . . .

1. ....

2. ....

3. ....

4. ....

5. ....

My 3 month goals . . .

1. ....
2. ....
3. ....

My wild outrageous goals . . .

1. ....
2. ....
3. ....
4. ....
5. ....
6. ....
7. ....
8. ....
9. ....
10. ....

My intention for today . . .

....
....
....
....
....

Evening Reflection . . . Wins for the day

1. ....
2. ....
3. ....
4. ....
5. ....

My Beautiful Morning

"Don't worry about being successful but work toward being significant and the success will naturally follow."

~Oprah Winfrey

Date:

Morning Intentions

I am ....

I enjoy ....

I give ....

I complete ....

I forgive ....

I am grateful for . . .

1. ....

2. ....

3. ....

4. ....

5. ....

My 3 month goals...

1. ....
2. ....
3. ....

My wild outrageous goals...

1. ....
2. ....
3. ....
4. ....
5. ....
6. ....
7. ....
8. ....
9. ....
10. ....

My intention for today...

....
....
....
....

Evening Reflection... Wins for the day

1. ....
2. ....
3. ....
4. ....
5. ....

My Beautiful Morning

"The only limit to the height of your achievements is the reach of your dreams and the willingness to work hard for them."

~Michelle Obama

Date: ....

Morning Intentions

I am ....

I enjoy ....

I give ....

I complete ....

I forgive ....

I am grateful for . . .

1. ....
2. ....
3. ....
4. ....
5. ....

My 3 month goals . . .

1. ....
2. ....
3. ....

My wild outrageous goals . . .

1. ....
2. ....
3. ....
4. ....
5. ....
6. ....
7. ....
8. ....
9. ....
10. ....

My intention for today . . .

....
....
....
....
....

Evening Reflection . . . Wins for the day

1. ....
2. ....
3. ....
4. ....
5. ....

My Beautiful Morning

"Opportunities don't happen.
You create them."

~Chris Grosser

Date:

Morning Intentions

I am ....

I enjoy ....

I give ....

I complete ....

I forgive ....

I am grateful for . . .

1. ....

2. ....

3. ....

4. ....

5. ....

My 3 month goals . . .

1. ....
2. ....
3. ....

My wild outrageous goals . . .

1. ....
2. ....
3. ....
4. ....
5. ....
6. ....
7. ....
8. ....
9. ....
10. ....

My intention for today . . .

....
....
....
....

Evening Reflection . . . Wins for the day

1. ....
2. ....
3. ....
4. ....
5. ....

My Beautiful Morning

"Setting goals is the first step in turning the invisible into the visible."

~Tony Robbins

Date:

Morning Intentions

I am ....

I enjoy ....

I give ....

I complete ....

I forgive ....

I am grateful for . . .

1. ....

2. ....

3. ....

4. ....

5. ....

My 3 month goals . . .

1. ....
2. ....
3. ....

My wild outrageous goals . . .

1. ....
2. ....
3. ....
4. ....
5. ....
6. ....
7. ....
8. ....
9. ....
10. ....

My intention for today . . .

....
....
....
....

Evening Reflection . . . Wins for the day

1. ....
2. ....
3. ....
4. ....
5. ....

My Beautiful Morning

"All our dreams can come true, if we
have the courage to pursue them."

~Walt Disney

Date:

Morning Intentions

I am ....

I enjoy ....

I give ....

I complete ....

I forgive ....

I am grateful for . . .

1. ....

2. ....

3. ....

4. ....

5. ....

My 3 month goals . . .

1. ....
2. ....
3. ....

My wild outrageous goals . . .

1. ....
2. ....
3. ....
4. ....
5. ....
6. ....
7. ....
8. ....
9. ....
10. ....

My intention for today . . .

....

....

....

....

Evening Reflection . . . Wins for the day

1. ....
2. ....
3. ....
4. ....
5. ....

My Beautiful Morning

"Successful people do what unsuccessful people are not willing to do. Don't wish it were easier; wish you were better."

~Jim Rohn

Date:

Morning Intentions

I am ....

I enjoy ....

I give ....

I complete ....

I forgive ....

I am grateful for . . .

1. ....

2. ....

3. ....

4. ....

5. ....

My 3 month goals . . .

1. ....
2. ....
3. ....

My wild outrageous goals . . .

1. ....
2. ....
3. ....
4. ....
5. ....
6. ....
7. ....
8. ....
9. ....
10. ....

My intention for today . . .

....
....
....
....

Evening Reflection . . . Wins for the day

1. ....
2. ....
3. ....
4. ....
5. ....

My Beautiful Morning

"I believe the last thing I read at night will likely manifest when I'm sleeping. You become what you think about the most."

~Daymond John

Date: ....

Morning Intentions

I am ....

I enjoy ....

I give ....

I complete ....
....

I forgive ....
....

I am grateful for . . .

1. ....

2. ....

3. ....

4. ....

5. ....

My 3 month goals . . .

1. ....
2. ....
3. ....

My wild outrageous goals . . .

1. ....
2. ....
3. ....
4. ....
5. ....
6. ....
7. ....
8. ....
9. ....
10. ....

My intention for today . . .

....
....
....
....

Evening Reflection . . . Wins for the day

1. ....
2. ....
3. ....
4. ....
5. ....

My Beautiful Morning

"I believe that if you'll just stand up and go, life will open up for you. Something just motivates you to keep moving."

~Tina Turner

Date:

Morning Intentions

I am ....

I enjoy ....

I give ....

I complete ....

I forgive ....

I am grateful for . . .

1. ....

2. ....

3. ....

4. ....

5. ....

My 3 month goals . . .

1. ....
2. ....
3. ....

My wild outrageous goals . . .

1. ....
2. ....
3. ....
4. ....
5. ....
6. ....
7. ....
8. ....
9. ....
10. ....

My intention for today . . .

....
....
....
....
....

Evening Reflection . . . Wins for the day

1. ....
2. ....
3. ....
4. ....
5. ....

My Beautiful Morning

"Success is walking from failure to failure with no loss of enthusiasm."

~Winston Churchill

Date:

Morning Intentions

I am ....

I enjoy ....

I give ....

I complete ....

I forgive ....

I am grateful for . . .

1. ....

2. ....

3. ....

4. ....

5. ....

My 3 month goals . . .

1. ....
2. ....
3. ....

My wild outrageous goals . . .

1. ....
2. ....
3. ....
4. ....
5. ....
6. ....
7. ....
8. ....
9. ....
10. ....

My intention for today . . .

....
....
....
....

Evening Reflection . . . Wins for the day

1. ....
2. ....
3. ....
4. ....
5. ....

My Beautiful Morning

"You measure the size of the accomplishment
by the obstacles you have to overcome
to reach your goals."

~Booker T. Washington

Date:

Morning Intentions

I am ....

I enjoy ....

I give ....

I complete ....

I forgive ....

I am grateful for . . .

1. ....

2. ....

3. ....

4. ....

5. ....

My 3 month goals . . .

1. ....
2. ....
3. ....

My wild outrageous goals . . .

1. ....
2. ....
3. ....
4. ....
5. ....
6. ....
7. ....
8. ....
9. ....
10. ....

My intention for today . . .

....
....
....
....

Evening Reflection . . . Wins for the day

1. ....
2. ....
3. ....
4. ....
5. ....

My Beautiful Morning

*"You've got to follow that dream,
wherever that dream may lead."*

~Elvis Presley

Date:

Morning Intentions

I am ....

I enjoy ....

I give ....

I complete ....

I forgive ....

I am grateful for . . .

1. ....

2. ....

3. ....

4. ....

5. ....

My 3 month goals . . .

1. ....
2. ....
3. ....

My wild outrageous goals . . .

1. ....
2. ....
3. ....
4. ....
5. ....
6. ....
7. ....
8. ....
9. ....
10. ....

My intention for today . . .

....
....
....
....
....

Evening Reflection . . . Wins for the day

1. ....
2. ....
3. ....
4. ....
5. ....

My Beautiful Morning

"Don't let the fear of losing be greater
than the excitement of winning."

~Robert Kiyosaki

Date:

Morning Intentions

I am ....

I enjoy ....

I give ....

I complete ....

I forgive ....

I am grateful for . . .

1. ....

2. ....

3. ....

4. ....

5. ....

My 3 month goals . . .

1. ....
2. ....
3. ....

My wild outrageous goals . . .

1. ....
2. ....
3. ....
4. ....
5. ....
6. ....
7. ....
8. ....
9. ....
10. ....

My intention for today . . .

....
....
....
....

Evening Reflection . . . Wins for the day

1. ....
2. ....
3. ....
4. ....
5. ....

My Beautiful Morning

"You are never too old to set another goal or to dream a new dream."

~C.S. Lewis

Date:

Morning Intentions

I am ....

I enjoy ....

I give ....

I complete ....

I forgive ....

I am grateful for . . .

1. ....

2. ....

3. ....

4. ....

5. ....

My 3 month goals . . .

1. ....
2. ....
3. ....

My wild outrageous goals . . .

1. ....
2. ....
3. ....
4. ....
5. ....
6. ....
7. ....
8. ....
9. ....
10. ....

My intention for today . . .

....
....
....
....

Evening Reflection . . . Wins for the day

1. ....
2. ....
3. ....
4. ....
5. ....

My Beautiful Morning

"There is a powerful driving force inside every human being that once unleashed can make any vision, dream, or desire a reality."

~Anthony Robbins

Date: _____

Morning Intentions

I am ....

I enjoy ....

I give ....

I complete ....

I forgive ....

I am grateful for . . .

1. ....

2. ....

3. ....

4. ....

5. ....

My 3 month goals . . .

1. . . . .
2. . . . .
3. . . . .

My wild outrageous goals . . .

1. . . . .
2. . . . .
3. . . . .
4. . . . .
5. . . . .
6. . . . .
7. . . . .
8. . . . .
9. . . . .
10. . . . .

My intention for today . . .

. . . .
. . . .
. . . .
. . . .

Evening Reflection . . . Wins for the day

1. . . . .
2. . . . .
3. . . . .
4. . . . .
5. . . . .

My Beautiful Morning

"Cherish your visions and your dreams as they are the children of your soul, the blueprints of your ultimate achievements."

~Napoleon Hill

Date: ....

Morning Intentions

I am ....

I enjoy ....

I give ....

I complete ....

I forgive ....

I am grateful for . . .

1. ....

2. ....

3. ....

4. ....

5. ....

My 3 month goals . . .

1. ....
2. ....
3. ....

My wild outrageous goals . . .

1. ....
2. ....
3. ....
4. ....
5. ....
6. ....
7. ....
8. ....
9. ....
10. ....

My intention for today . . .

....
....
....
....

Evening Reflection . . . Wins for the day

1. ....
2. ....
3. ....
4. ....
5. ....

My Beautiful Morning

"The biggest adventure you can take is to live the life of your dreams."

~Oprah Winfrey

Date:

Morning Intentions

I am ....

I enjoy ....

I give ....

I complete ....

I forgive ....

I am grateful for . . .

1. ....

2. ....

3. ....

4. ....

5. ....

My 3 month goals . . .

1. ....
2. ....
3. ....

My wild outrageous goals . . .

1. ....
2. ....
3. ....
4. ....
5. ....
6. ....
7. ....
8. ....
9. ....
10. ....

My intention for today . . .

....
....
....
....
....

Evening Reflection . . . Wins for the day

1. ....
2. ....
3. ....
4. ....
5. ....

My Beautiful Morning

"Sometimes a dream almost whispers, it never shouts. So you have to, every day of your lives, be ready to hear what whispers in your ear."

~ Steven Spielberg

Date:

Morning Intentions

I am ....

I enjoy ....

I give ....

I complete ....

I forgive ....

I am grateful for . . .

1. ....

2. ....

3. ....

4. ....

5. ....

My 3 month goals . . .

1. ....
2. ....
3. ....

My wild outrageous goals . . .

1. ....
2. ....
3. ....
4. ....
5. ....
6. ....
7. ....
8. ....
9. ....
10. ....

My intention for today . . .

....
....
....
....

Evening Reflection . . . Wins for the day

1. ....
2. ....
3. ....
4. ....
5. ....

My Beautiful Morning

"Envision, create, and believe in your own universe, and the universe will form around you."

~Tony Hsieh

Date: _____

Morning Intentions

I am ....

I enjoy ....

I give ....

I complete ....

I forgive ....

I am grateful for . . .

1. ....

2. ....

3. ....

4. ....

5. ....

My 3 month goals . . .

1. ....
2. ....
3. ....

My wild outrageous goals . . .

1. ....
2. ....
3. ....
4. ....
5. ....
6. ....
7. ....
8. ....
9. ....
10. ....

My intention for today . . .

....
....
....
....

Evening Reflection . . . Wins for the day

1. ....
2. ....
3. ....
4. ....
5. ....

My Beautiful Morning

"Keep your heart open to dreams. For as long as there's a dream, there is hope, and as long as there is hope, there is joy in living."

~Anonymus

Date: ....

Morning Intentions

I am ....

I enjoy ....

I give ....

I complete ....

I forgive ....

I am grateful for . . .

1. ....

2. ....

3. ....

4. ....

5. ....

My 3 month goals . . .

1. ....
2. ....
3. ....

My wild outrageous goals . . .

1. ....
2. ....
3. ....
4. ....
5. ....
6. ....
7. ....
8. ....
9. ....
10. ....

My intention for today . . .

....
....
....
....

Evening Reflection . . . Wins for the day

1. ....
2. ....
3. ....
4. ....
5. ....

My Beautiful Morning

"Life is full of beauty. Notice it. Notice the bumble bee, the small child, and the smiling faces. Smell the rain, and feel the wind. Live your life to the fullest potential, and fight for your dreams."

~Ashley Smith

Date:

Morning Intentions

I am ....

I enjoy ....

I give ....

I complete ....

I forgive ....

I am grateful for . . .

1. ....

2. ....

3. ....

4. ....

5. ....

My 3 month goals . . .

1. ....
2. ....
3. ....

My wild outrageous goals . . .

1. ....
2. ....
3. ....
4. ....
5. ....
6. ....
7. ....
8. ....
9. ....
10. ....

My intention for today . . .

....
....
....
....

Evening Reflection . . . Wins for the day

1. ....
2. ....
3. ....
4. ....
5. ....

MEET THE AUTHOR
TREZ IBRAHIM

Trez Ibrahim, Founder and CEO of Life Mastery Solution and TI International, is the world's leading Evolutionary Strategist and Spiritual Catalyst working with some of the most prominent business owners, executives, and entrepreneurs in the world.

She is a Trainer, Author, Speaker, Business and Executive Coach with over 30 years of experience in Excellence and High Performance. Her mission? To empower men and women to Escape the Ordinary, Discover Their Bliss, Create Massive Success & Find Freedom Within. She believes that every man and woman deserves to feel connected to his and her body, magnetize and create extraordinary results, radiate with confidence and live the life of her dreams.

Her current home is located in Southern California where she enjoys fabulous weather year round. Read her story on her website at https://lifemasterysolution.com/about/

"If there's a book that you want to read, but it hasn't been written yet, then you must write it."

HAVE QUESTIONS?

360 East First Street, Suite 426
Tustin, CA 92780
info@LifeMasterySolution.com
www.LifeMasterySolution.com

FB.COM/TREZIBRAHIM1

IG.COM/TREZ_IBRAHIM

TREZIBRAHIM.COM

LINKEDIN.COM/IN/TREZ-IBRAHIM

TWITTER.COM/TREZIBRAHIM

WWW.LIFEMASTERYSOLUTION.COM

Made in the USA
Middletown, DE
08 April 2022

63729694R00046